Marine Aquaculture and the Landscape:

The siting and design of marine aquaculture developments in the landscape

Natural Heritage Management

CONTENTS   Page

MARINE AQUACULTURE AND THE LANDSCAPE: The siting and design of marine aquaculture developments in the landscape
16 February 2000. Prepared by Alison Grant, Landscape Architect, for Scottish Natural Heritage, the Crown Estate and Scottish Quality Salmon.

Marine Aquaculture and the Landscape

INTRODUCTION

Marine fin fish and shellfish farming in Scotland is now well established. While salmon and mussel farming are still the mainstay of the industry, there is constant innovation in methods of production. Experiments with farming other fish and constant developments in scale of operating, feeding technology, growth stimulants and safety requirements, mean that this dynamic industry is continuing to expand and develop.

The search for new sites puts pressure on other land and sea based industries and, particularly, on the environment.

This guidance offers advice on how to assess and address the landscape and visual impact of marine aquaculture developments. It does not deal with the other environmental, social or economic issues raised by this type of development. It aims to ensure that those involved in aquaculture developments are well informed on landscape issues, and provides them with a clear framework for making positive decisions about the siting and design of both onshore and marine-based facilities.

Nevertheless, in some circumstances, where landscapes are complicated in character or sensitive to change, developers should consider employing a landscape architect to advise on the potential landscape impacts of a proposal and how these might be resolved.

Landscape

We are all responsible for maintaining and enhancing a landscape of quality and exceptional diversity of character in Scotland. It is of benefit to all industries that this clean and attractive environment is managed sympathetically, and with broad social, economic, cultural and environmental needs in mind.

As a result, this guidance places particular emphasis **on the need to identify an appropriate location for development in the first place**. As the industry expands, it will become more difficult to identify new locations where landscape can accommodate the scale and nature of this type of development. In addition, the incremental expansion of individual fish and shellfish farms will be increasingly difficult to accommodate within the relatively intimate scale of Scotland's coastline. Nevertheless, well located developments can positively contribute to landscape character, and create opportunities to reinforce the landscape as a working environment.

Perceived wildness and sense of remoteness are valued as a diminishing resource, but in addition, the rich variety and distinctiveness of the character of all our landscapes is recognised as an important asset. **All developments are expected to respect the diversity of landscape character and sustain the qualities which reinforce experience of place**. With careful siting and layout, aquaculture can make a positive contribution to revitalising the landscape, for example through reusing redundant buildings and introducing an energising sense of human activity.

The nature of Scotland's coastline means that aquaculture development is often highly visible, either from land or sea. The importance of visibility, whether in relation to classic vistas, or as a contribution to the experience of place, cannot be underestimated. **Aquaculture should not need to be hidden from view, but should be well enough sited and designed to fit in with the surrounding character and contribute to a lived in landscape.**

The Aims of this Guidance

With this in mind, the aims of this guidance are to:
- give advice on how to determine the most appropriate location for aquaculture development in relation to the landscape;
- indicate and explain issues of landscape significance which may need to be addressed in an Environmental Impact Assessment (EIA);
- explain how to assess the landscape and visual impacts of aquaculture development;
- offer guidance on how to site and design aquaculture developments to reduce both their visual impact and their impact on landscape character;
- encourage the aquaculture industry to consider landscape character and design issues during the ongoing management and development of existing sites.

The Role of Consultees

Aquaculture development requires authorisation before it can be established. During this process, both Scottish Natural Heritage (SNH) and Local Planning Authorities will pay particular attention to the potential impact of a proposal on the landscape.

Moreover, Local Planning Authorities expect applications for planning permission to contain supporting evidence in relation to economic and environmental issues.

In the future, therefore, when Local Authorities have responsibility for authorising aquaculture developments, applicants should be prepared to offer such evidence. The guidance offered in this document may be used to assist in the identification and presentation of landscape evidence when preparing planning applications.

This report was commissioned by SNH, the Crown Estate (CE) and Scottish Quality Salmon (SQS) and has involved consultation with representatives of the industry and the planning authorities.

It is expected to be used by both those who develop and manage aquaculture facilities and those who comment on applications for development.

Information on the procedures relating to authorising aquaculture developments can be found in the draft Procedure Guidance Note issued by SOAEFD (SERAD's predecessor), entitled 'Interim Scheme for the Authorisation of Marine Fish Farms in Scottish Waters'.

How to Use This Guidance

This guidance is divided into three sections, which reflect the key decisions a potential developer makes when locating, siting and designing aquaculture development.

The first section explains **how to identify an appropriate location for development from a landscape perspective**. It outlines the locational guidance available, and identifies the key issues of strategic significance to consider when assessing potential development within a broad landscape area.

The second section goes on to **explain landscape character and visual assessment** in detail. It highlights the issues most relevant to the siting and layout of aquaculture development within a chosen location.

The third section illustrates **detail design considerations**, including those which relate to the onshore facilities which may accompany some offshore developments.

Finally, this report complements other published documents. Appendix 1 illustrates in tabular form what these other documents contain, and from where they can be obtained.

Section 1: CHOOSING A LOCATION

Scotland is a small country. While its coastline is relatively extensive, it is often intimate in scale and highly visible. A series of small scale developments can quickly make a disproportionately much larger impact in such a landscape. Likewise, even one development located in a landscape valued for its special scenic or wild land qualities, may erode the national resource of these now relatively rare landscapes.

Choosing an appropriate location for development is therefore the first, and perhaps the most important, step in ensuring that aquaculture development fits in well with the landscape.

The location is the general area within which a development will be sited. When first considering aquaculture development, developers should assess a number of potential locations, possibly along a length of coastline and within a number of lochs. This will ensure that at an early stage:

- areas where aquaculture development is inappropriate in principle are identified;
- issues of landscape significance which might indicate the need for an EIA can be identified at an early stage;
- the national and regional significance of the landscape of the area is well understood in relation to potential development.

This section explains the issues which should be addressed when assessing the potential opportunities and constraints of a location. This process should take into account the following issues:

- national locational guidance
- framework plans prepared by Local Authorities
- designations
- landscape character assessment
- cumulative impact
- remoteness
- visual impact

At this stage, Local Authorities and SNH can advise on the possible landscape issues associated with developing certain locations.

National Locational Guidance

The Government has produced draft locational guidance for marine fish farms which takes into account advice about landscape as well as other environmental issues. It categorises the Scottish coastline into:

- Category One Areas, 'where the development of new or the expansion of existing marine fish farms will only be acceptable in exceptional circumstances'[1];
- Category Two Areas, 'where the prospects for further substantial developments are likely to be limited'[1];
- Other Areas, 'where there appear to be better prospects of satisfying environmental requirements'[1].

Maps and more detailed information about these areas are set out in the Government's Policy Guidance Note 'Locational Guidelines for the Authorisation of Marine Fish Farms in Scottish Waters', available from the Fisheries Group at SERAD.

Framework Plans

Non statutory marine fish farm framework plans for parts of the Scottish coastline may be available from Local Authorities.

Framework plans build on the Local Authority policies and seek to balance the needs of competing interests along the coast, although the recommendations specifically apply to aquaculture development.

They are useful for **finding out what the Local Authority policy on the location and siting of fish farms is for specific areas,** because their policies are linked to geographic areas illustrated in an accompanying map. These zoned policies take into account landscape as well as other interests.

Designations

An area is designated because it contains characteristics or features which are particularly valued. This does not mean that aquaculture cannot take place within a designated area, but it does mean that **any development will need to be very sensitive to the interests for which the designation has been put in place.**

The most significant designations in relation to landscape are:

- National Scenic Areas (NSAs), which are landscapes designated at a national level because of their outstanding scenic quality - these are areas where the landscape is recognised as being particularly spectacular in a Scottish context;
- regional landscape designations, which are designated by Local Authorities - these are areas which are considered to be regionally important in terms of their character and visual quality;
- in the future - these lochs and stretches of coastline may contain National Parks.

Information on these designations is available from Local Planning Authorities. SNH also has an important role as guardian of NSAs, and the local office will be able to offer advice on proposals which are likely to affect the scenic qualities of individual NSAs.

[1] Scottish Executive Rural Affairs Department Policy Guidance Note 'Locational Guidelines for the Authorisation of Marine Fish Farms in Scottish Waters.'

Aquaculture development may compromise the landscape objectives of a landscape designation. A proposal may adversely impact on the scenic qualities or on the integrity of the specific landscape character which is valued and which has led to the designation being put in place. It is likely that some consultees will object to the proposed development in principle in these circumstances.

Potential developers are therefore strongly advised to seek advice from the **Local Authority and SNH at an early stage if a development is likely to impact upon a designated area**.

Landscape Character Assessment

Physical character, human activity, visual qualities and experience of place often combine to create a landscape character which is distinct across a geographic area.

One of the aims of locating and designing a development with care, is to ensure that the proposal does not undermine characteristics which contribute most significantly to the landscape character of an area. Where possible, new developments should relate to the key characteristics of an area. The process by which these key characteristics are identified and assessed is called landscape character assessment.

A national programme of landscape character assessment has been undertaken by SNH which now covers the whole of Scotland. Individual landscape character assessment reports (LCAs) are available from SNH.

The LCAs aim to provide a greater understanding of landscape character through providing information about landscape character in distinctive geographic areas. Using LCAs, potential developers should be able to identify the landscape character type of their potential sites, and consider how their development will affect the key characteristics. LCAs also offer guidance on how development may relate to the key characteristics of an area.

When choosing a location, potential developers **should find LCAs particularly helpful in assessing the sensitivity of different landscape character types to changes brought about by new developments and changes in land use**. In addition, LCAs which cover coastal areas may offer specific advice about the siting and design of aquaculture developments in relation to coastal landscape character types.

Cumulative Impact

Where there is existing aquaculture, both new proposals and extensions to existing developments may be difficult to accommodate within the landscape. LCAs may indicate which landscape character types cannot easily accommodate cumulative aquaculture development.

It may be that there are apparently no aquaculture developments near the sites being considered. However, the Crown Estate can provide information on both existing leases for development which may have not yet been developed, and also applications which are under consideration.

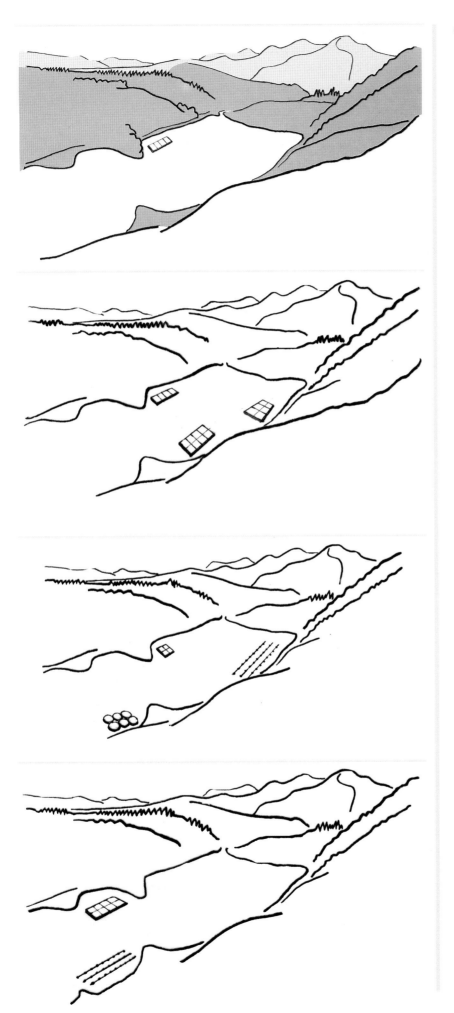

- The impact of one well designed, perhaps relatively small scale proposal may be absorbed by the scale of the landscape. **Sometimes a future extension, or additional developments may dominate the space within which they are sited**.

- Several developments together can attract more attention, creating a strong focus within the landscape.

- Whereas one individual development may act as a landscape feature, a **number of developments can create a key characteristic of the landscape**, altering the landscape character.

- When a **number of developments** which occupy the same loch are **not coordinated** in terms of siting, layout and design, **the effect can be muddled and visually confusing**.

- Where a number of small inlets or bays are gradually filled up with development, **the important indentations along the coastline become obscure**, resulting in a change of landscape character.

Remoteness and Wild Land

Areas which are distant from settlements and obvious human activity often have qualities of remoteness which may be reinforced by the lack of accessibility. These qualities are increasingly rare and frequently contribute significantly to both the scenic quality and the landscape character of a place. They are valued by both residents and visitors alike.

Some areas are increasingly valued because of their wild land qualities. This sometimes, but not always, coincides with a degree of remoteness, and can certainly be linked to inaccessibility. It is reinforced by a sense of sanctuary and solitude, and a high degree of naturalness. Wild land qualities are engendered through the experience and perception of a place, not simply a physical separation from human settlement. LCAs may identify landscape character types which possess qualities of wild land or remote character.

Aquaculture development can be accessed by sea, and therefore can be proposed for relatively undeveloped areas, with little or no direct road access. The very inaccessibility of such areas may reinforce qualities which create either a sense of remoteness or wild land.

In such areas, it is likely to be inappropriate to introduce any aquaculture development. This is because it is not just the visual impact of the proposal which is likely to be of concern. It is also the movement, noise of boats and generators and ongoing management activity which will affect the experience and perception of such areas.

Onshore facilities, access tracks and power supplies as well as water based structures are also likely to impact upon a sense of wildness. It may be that in some cases, the water based element of a proposal can be accommodated, whilst road access or a shore base cannot without unacceptable adverse impacts.

Any developer considering locating structures in an area of remote or wild land character should contact the Planning Authority and SNH at an early stage.

Visual Impact

Structures in and on the water are often very visible due to:

- the contrast in texture between the cages or lines and the smooth, reflective surface of the water, particularly in calm weather;
- the contrast between the vertical sides of cages and infrastructure and the flat water surface;
- the constant changes in light conditions which one moment can cast a structure into shadow, and the next reflect bright light upon it;
- the changes in sea colour and tone which can often camouflage the structures one moment, but then emphasise the structure in dramatic contrast the next;
- the contrast between the often very regular and geometric shape and alignment of cages or lines and the more organic shape of the landform and coastline.

As a result, **water based development will often be difficult to miss, reinforcing the need to choose an appropriate location**. This does not mean that structures should always be removed from view, but an assessment of visual impact should be an integral stage of choosing a preferred location for development. To do this, the extent of visibility of potential locations for both water based and if necessary, onshore facilities, should be identified using maps and site survey.

The impact of potential onshore and water based developments from significant viewpoints should also be considered. Significant viewpoints include:

- views from a popular road or a route promoted as a tourist attraction;
- established settlements;
- well used vantage points;
- coastal footpaths;
- popular ferry routes;
- sites or villages of historic, architectural or cultural importance where the setting is important for visitor experience.

In some circumstances it may be inappropriate to locate any development within sight of a significant viewpoint. This can only be determined on an individual case basis. **If in doubt, potential developers should consult with the Planning Authority, SNH or Historic Scotland as appropriate at an early stage**.

For further information on undertaking visual assessment see pages 27-29.

When choosing a location for development, a developer should consider, and where necessary obtain advice from the Crown Estate, on the process by which the need for an Environmental Impact Assessment (EIA) may be established. It is likely that any significant adverse impacts on landscape associated with the location of a development will lead to a request for an EIA.

Guidance on the preparation of an EIA can be found in the publication 'Environmental Assessment Guidance Manual for Marine Salmon Farmers', available from the Crown Estate. Copies of the EIA Regulations, which set out the statutory requirements, are available from the Scottish Executive Rural Affairs Department .

A checklist of steps to be considered when undertaking the landscape component of an Environmental Impact Assessment is given in Box 1.

BOX 1: Environmental Impact Assessment

In preparing the landscape component of an Environmental Impact Assessment (EIA), a developer should carry out the following steps:

- Attend a scoping meeting with consultees at the outset, which for landscape interests will include the Local Authority and SNH, and may include other local groups. Consultees should at this stage be able to provide an indication of what landscape interests they wish to see addressed in the EIA.
- Demonstrate the options which have been considered for locating the proposed development, including an explanation of why the particular location has been chosen. This explanation should include environmental as well as economic, social and practical considerations.
- Explain how the proposal relates to National Planning Guidelines, Local Authority Framework plans and planning policies, and the policies of other consultees.
- Describe the location of the proposal in relation to designated areas within or close to which the site is located, and the impact it will have on the qualities for which the areas have been designated.

In addition to the above, developers are required to present both an assessment of the impact of a scheme on landscape and the mitigating measures which have been taken to reduce any identified impacts. The EIA is therefore also likely to include the following details:

- Information from the appropriate LCA, including how the relevant advice and guidance has been used to help locate and design the proposal.
- An explanation of how the proposed scheme relates to the landscape character of the area.
- If appropriate, an explanation of how the proposal will avoid creating an adverse cumulative impact on the landscape.
- If the proposal is to be located in a remote area, or an area valued for its wild land qualities, there should be an assessment of how it will affect these qualities, and how they are to be mitigated.
- A map indicating key viewpoints, accompanied by illustrations such as photomontages, sketches or acetate overlays on photographs. These should illustrate how the proposal will be seen in context.
- Maps could also be used to demonstrate the extent to which the potential development is visible from settlements, roads, footpaths, ferries and key water routes.

LANDSCAPE CHARACTER

The landscapes of Scotland are a rich physical and scenic resource. Industries depend on this diversity and individuals are inspired by it. New development of all kinds should respond sensitively to the quality and variety of coastal landscapes, aiming to respect both the range of character types and the scenic qualities which make each area distinctive.

Understanding the character of the landscape and how it is experienced is a first step towards siting and planning the layout of a fish farm or shellfish line proposal. In particular, character assessment should assist in:

- planning the scale of the development;
- positioning both onshore and water-based structures;
- aligning the water-based structures;
- planning the layout and scale of both the water based structures and any necessary onshore facilities and infrastructure.

Scottish Natural Heritage Landscape Character Assessments

Scottish Natural Heritage has recently completed a programme of landscape character assessment which covers the whole of Scotland. The Landscape Character Assessments (LCAs) for individual parts of Scotland are available in report form from SNH. Developers should consult the assessment which covers the area of the proposed development when considering the siting and layout of aquaculture installations.

LCAs provide information on the key characteristics of specific landscape character types and also provide guidance on landscape change and the design of developments within each landscape character type. Some LCAs also provide specific guidance on how to relate aquaculture developments to the landscape character.

Using LCAs, potential developers should be able to identify in which landscape character type their proposal lies, and what possibilities there are for relating their development to the landscape characteristics.

Using This Section

The following guidance complements the LCAs by setting out how to integrate aquaculture with the principal landscape characteristics of the Scottish coastline. It does this by describing three broad categories of coastal landscape character, and illustrating what to consider when siting and aligning both water-based and onshore structures.

The three broad categories of landscape character are:
- Steep sided, enclosed loch
- Sheltered but expansive lochs
- Coasts

Developers should use this section by reading the descriptions of each broad landscape character category. They should identify which category of coastline is most similar to their chosen location for development. Some locations may have characteristics which are in more than one category, and will need to study the guidance set out in more than one character category.

The guidance on siting and layout appropriate to each category follow each character description.

This section also describes the implications of settlement pattern on aquaculture developments, and what to consider when assessing the visual impact of an individual proposal.

STEEP SIDED, ENCLOSED LOCHS

Key Characteristics

- The coastline is dominated by the **steep sides of mountains** which plunge into the sea, creating a sense of drama.
- The steep sided topography can **create dense shadow**, and the sheltered, often calm waters offer opportunities for **distinct reflections**.
- Often this landscape type is characterised by **the sense of enclosure** and intimacy, emphasised by the verticality of the surrounding landform.
- Views are concentrated **along the length of, or directly across, the loch**, rather than along the hill tops.
- The coastline of these lochs is often **relatively simple**, with few indentations.
- Roads often approach these lochs over high passes, **giving elevated views**, or are constrained by the steep landform and are located close to the loch side, **resulting in views directly across the loch**.
- Bridging points at the head of the lochs are often **focal points** in the landscape.

Implications for siting and layout

In these relatively narrow, intimate lochs, the simplicity, scale and expanse of the water surface is important. Too many water-based structures, or one large development can quickly lead to overcrowding, and divert views away from the central loch space.

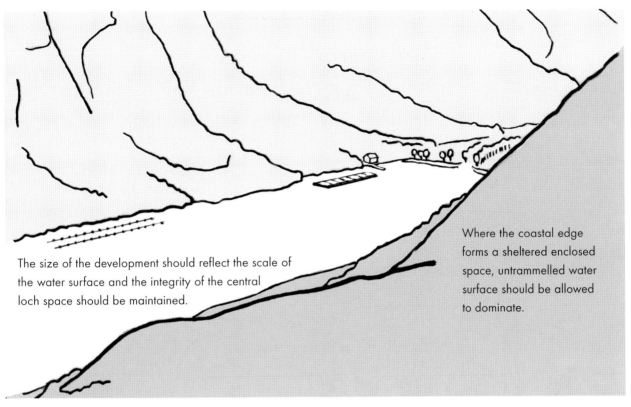

The size of the development should reflect the scale of the water surface and the integrity of the central loch space should be maintained.

Where the coastal edge forms a sheltered enclosed space, untrammelled water surface should be allowed to dominate.

- Structures sited across the loch space may fragment and subdivide the loch, breaking up its simple expanse. **Structures should therefore be aligned parallel to the long length of the loch, not across it.**

- Often in steep sided enclosed lochs, the coastal edge is simple in shape, with relatively few indentations. **Cages and lines should aim to reflect this characteristic and appear as simple, linear shapes.**

- Owing to the steep sides of these enclosed lochs, often there are areas which are in deep shadow for much of the day. **New shore-based facilities will be less obvious if sited against a backdrop of shadows and rising ground.**

- Excavation of landform on steep slopes for access tracks or shore bases can cause considerable long term scarring of the landscape. **Development should aim to site shore-based facilities where they do not result in excessive earth moving.** Appropriate sites tend to be set back against a break in slope and away from promontories.

Key Characteristics

- These lochs are enclosed by hills or mountains but feel **less contained** because of the long length and wide breadth of the loch.
- The landform near to the water edge is **frequently gentle in gradient**, sometimes with low rocky outcrops or ledges, **creating a gradual transition from the flat water surface to the steeper hillsides**.
- Often, the eye is drawn to **a skyline of hill tops** over an expanse of water.
- The coastline is generally **indented with small bays** and sometimes islands or skerries.
- Roads are not constrained by landform so views from roads are often part of the way up the hillside, allowing **viewers to look down upon the water**.

Implications for siting and layout

In these landscapes, cages and lines can readily dominate the water surface of small bays and lochside indentations, resulting in the loss of a key characteristic. Often, the relative intimacy of the coastline makes it difficult to accommodate the mass of large cages or extensive areas of lines.

Cages and lines can reflect the horizontal emphasis in this landscape, by reinforcing the shape and alignments of promontories and landform spurs.

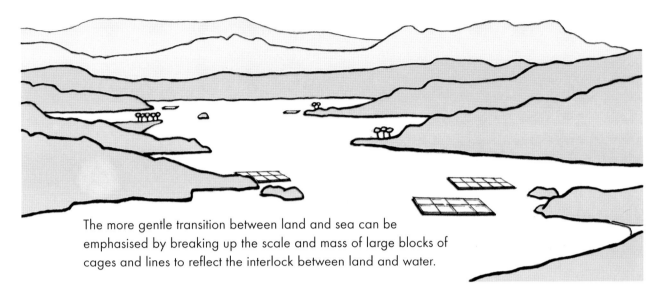

The more gentle transition between land and sea can be emphasised by breaking up the scale and mass of large blocks of cages and lines to reflect the interlock between land and water.

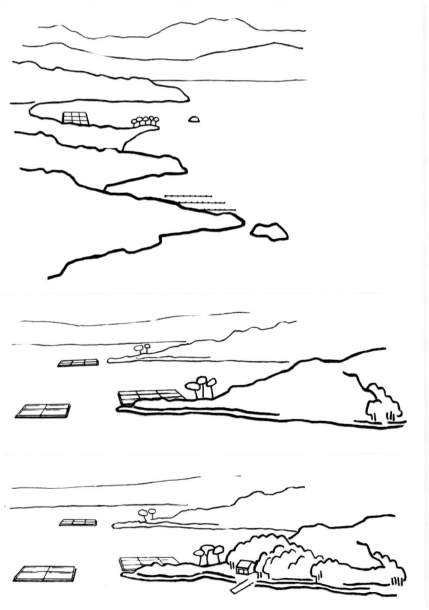

- Where a series of small bays create a distinctive landscape characteristic, filling in of successive small bays should be avoided. Where possible, **the majority of bays should be left free from development**, so that it is possible to visually follow the indented coast without obstruction.

- Cages and lines can quickly dominate the intimate scale of individual bays. The **open, expansive nature of the water surface area should still be allowed to dominate** when planning an aquaculture installation.

- Shore-based facilities may be able to **nestle into the rocky outcrops and low ledges around the gently graded coastline**. Often in this type of landscape, there are opportunities to establish woodland to link in with existing vegetation patterns.

Key Characteristics

- Coasts are **open to the sea**, and feel exposed.
- This coastal edge often forms **distinctive bays** and is often punctuated with **islands or skerries**.
- The landform around the coast is **often relatively gentle**, with low hills, rocky knolls and low sweeping headlands; however in some areas, the coastal edge is dominated by **rocky outcrops and cliffs**.
- Often this character type is dominated by **the horizontal line of the water**, and the sense of open space is emphasised by the expanse of sea.
- Views are often **panoramic**, embracing a wide sweep of seascape. Often, views along the coastal edge are partial, broken by headlands, islands and promontories.

Implications for siting and layout

In these landscapes, cages and lines which are too large or too numerous can visually coalesce, obscuring the distinct pattern and scale of skerries and the indented coastline.

22

Well scaled and sited cages can reflect the pattern and layout of skerries and islands. Aquaculture developments should reflect the subtleties of the shape and scale of the coastline.

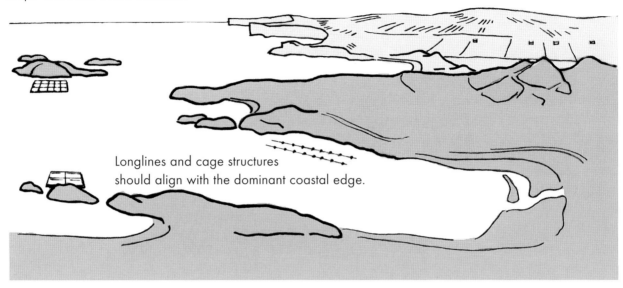

Longlines and cage structures should align with the dominant coastal edge.

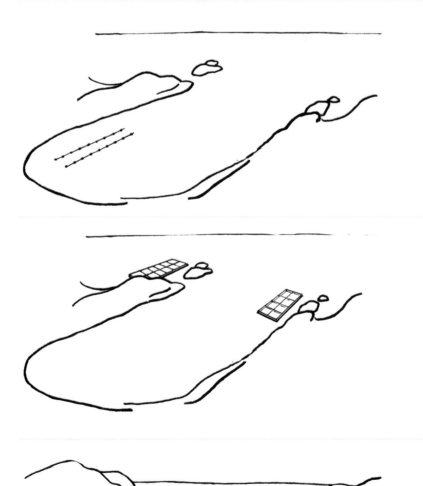

- Structures should avoid filling up a bay. The **open, expansive nature of the water surface area should still be allowed to dominate** when planning an aquaculture installation.

- Avoid siting a development where it appears to block the entrance to a bay, or separates a bay from the open sea – **a physical and visual link between the water contained within a bay and the open sea should be maintained**.

- **Shore bases should be sited low in the landscape,** avoiding promontories and with a backdrop of landform behind the buildings.

SETTLEMENT PATTERN

The three landscape character categories explained above will often contain some degree of settlement. The settlement pattern also contributes to landscape character, and can influence the siting and design of aquaculture proposals.

Concentrated settlements

Coastal villages can be linear, established along a lochside road, or clustered at the head of a loch at a key bridging point, or sheltered in a bay, with relatively easy access to the sea. **Often they form focal points within a landscape**.

It may be appropriate to locate shore-based facilities within or close by settlements. The infrastructure associated with shore bases, such as roads, storage yards and lighting, is more likely to be in keeping with the character of villages than remote, inaccessible landscapes.

While it is recognised that siting of shore bases within or near to settlements may result in longer boat journeys, there may be benefits in terms of the accessibility of infrastructure, landscape character and goodwill with residents who often like to see the activity and bustle associated with a thriving business.

● Shore-based facilities sited within, or near to concentrated settlements should be **sited to reflect the settlement pattern**.

Nevertheless, some activities associated with aquaculture can be unpopular. There can be problems with litter, discarded fish cages, unpleasant smells and increased traffic on small roads. Careful consideration of siting in relation to views from settlements and the interests of residents is essential.

Scattered settlement pattern

Scattered housing, often linked to a coastal road and the pattern of crofting land, creates a series of point features in the landscape. **This pattern can be very dispersed**. Again, the presence of established structures and activity in an area may help to integrate new structures and the noise and movement associated with fish farming.

Aquaculture developments can bring with them increased noise and traffic, and unwanted visual intrusion and smells. It is essential to consider the needs of residents when considering a proposal near to a settlement.

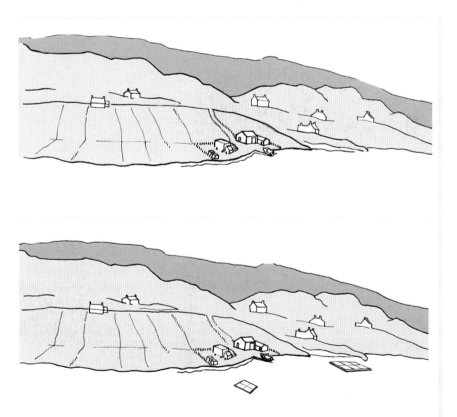

- Increasing the number of point features in the landscape can be a successful approach to integrating development, but care must be taken to **respect the scale and pattern of the existing features**.

- **Large scale blocks of cages or lines should be avoided near scattered settlements**, as the scale of the aquaculture installation will dominate the fragmented pattern of the settlement. Aquaculture development should reflect the scattered nature of the land-based structures.

Unsettled areas

It is difficult, and may not be desirable, to introduce new roads and buildings into areas which are characterised by their sense of remoteness from settlements, and where there are no existing buildings. Potential developers should consider other options carefully. Establishing a new shore base in areas of remote or wild land character should only be considered if no other viable options exist.

- Shore facilities will be more appropriate **in a nearby settlement**, rather than introducing a building and storage complex to an unsettled area.

- If there is no settlement pattern to follow, buildings should be integrated with the landform as far as possible. Buildings should **take advantage of level ground, be concentrated in layout, be set back against a break in slope, and set into a bay rather than on a promontory**.

VISUAL ASSESSMENT

A visual assessment is used to help identify an appropriate site, and to decide on a well proportioned and well designed lay out.

The visibility of the water-based structures and of any planned shore base should be considered in undertaking a visual assessment. In addition, all elements of the development, including access roads, food storage silos, lifting gear and other structures should be included.

An introduction to visual assessment, including identifying key viewpoints and assessing the significance of viewpoints is given in Section One, on page 15. In addition, a more detailed checklist of steps to be considered when undertaking a visual assessment is given in Box 2, which is on page 29.

Visual assessment allows developers to consider ways to link the proposal visually with the surrounding landscape, often by blending the structures into the colours and textures of the vegetation patterns, or by linking the siting of structures to landscape patterns.

To assess visual impact of aquaculture development, it is important to consider both **the eye level of the viewpoint and the proximity of the viewer to the development**.

● Cages viewed from a low level viewpoint are absorbed by background vegetation.

● The mass of these cages, sited close to the viewer, is broken up by the irregular outline of the cage layout

High level viewpoints

- From a high-level viewpoint, the contrast in texture between fish farm structures and the smooth, reflective surface of the water is more obvious. The geometric shapes of lines and cages are also clearly visible. It is also **very obvious if lines and cages are not parallel to the coast**.
- It is very important that the shape, scale, alignment and layout of cages **reflects the shape and scale of the coastline**.
- When viewed from a distance, aquaculture developments can be **visually linked to the pattern and texture of the vegetation**.

Low level viewpoints

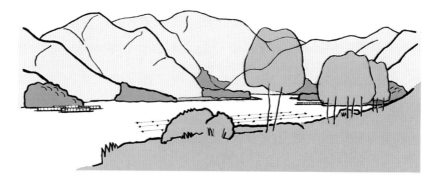

- From a low-level viewpoint, water-based structures can be **more easily absorbed into the landform and vegetation of the shore**. In particular, busy landscapes can create a backdrop which absorbs aquaculture installations relatively readily.
- When viewed close up, cages can dominate the water surface. Their **impact can be reduced by using an irregular pattern of cages** which varies the density of texture across the structure.

28

- If aquaculture installations are allowed to dominate the water surface in a sequence of views along a coast road, this can seem more intrusive than if it **is only in one view**.
- Views of water-based structures from coastal roads can be broken up by **planting along the shore line**. This approach is most successful where existing tree cover is part of the landscape character.
- Visual foreshortening occurs when the level surface of a large expanse of water takes up only a small part of a view. As a result, **vertical structures can have a high impact from a low-level viewpoint**.
- Structures such as overhead nets, rails and feed storage facilities contrast most significantly with the level water surface. They should be avoided where possible and **kept close to the water surface if they are essential.**

BOX 2: Visual Assessment

This guidance on undertaking visual assessment complements that given in other documents, in particular the 'Guidlines for Landscape and Visual Impact Assessment' published jointly by the Institute of Environmental Assessment and the Landscape Institute.

When assessing the potential visual impact of a proposal, developers should carry out the following steps:
- **Identify key viewpoints**, using a map based assessment, site survey or a computer visualisation programme.
- Draw up a map which illustrates **the extent of visibility and the proximity of viewpoints** to the development. This is called the zone of visual influence. Separate maps may be required for onshore and the water-based structures.
- Identify **the highest point in the development**, which may be a crane or a tall building. The zone of visual influence should take into account the visibility of this structure.
- Identify **how people view all elements of the development**. Are people walking, with sustained views of the proposal, or are they travelling by car, with the potential development glimpsed behind landform or trees?
- Consider how views will change **due to seasonal changes**, such as when trees lose their leaves, or when the summer sun is at its highest. Consider the impact of lighting.
- Identify whether or not the proposal has a significant effect on **the sequence of views experienced when travelling** along a road, footpath or established boat route.
- Identify whether the main views of a site are from **low-level vantage points** or from viewpoints which allow residents and visitors to **look down upon the site from above**.
- Consider whether views are mainly going to be **from a distance**, with the development set against a backdrop of hills or woodland, **or from a nearby viewpoint**, where the development will take up more of the view.
- Consider and illustrate how the **development is going to change over time**. For example, as the weight of the shellfish increases, the original, often quite small buoys need to be replaced with larger buoys. Consider the visual impact of the proposal when the development is at its most extensive.

All these considerations can be readily presented using maps, photographs, photomontages or computer generated perspectives. One of the simplest methods of illustrating a proposal and assessing its visual impact is to place acetate over a photographic panorama of the site, and to draw on the development at a realistic scale.

Section 3 : DETAIL DESIGN

The most successful aquaculture development will be arranged and designed to integrate with the landscape, through positively building on the landscape characteristics and by using the most appropriate detail design.

It is important to stress, however, **that no matter how well designed the structure is, if it is poorly located, badly sited or inappropriately laid out, it will not integrate with the landscape**. Well thought out detail design will not make up for a poor choice of location or a badly sited and laid out proposal. Detail design can only be of assistance once an appropriate location has been selected, and a layout has been planned which takes into account the surrounding landscape character.

When applying for authorisation to proceed with developing aquaculture, it is important that **all details of the development**, including the type of structures and food storage systems to be used, **are described**. In addition, it is important to consider not only what structures are required when a proposal is first submitted for approval, but **also how the structures will develop**. Any need for increased food storage capacity, potential requirements for expansion, and the use of larger buoys required for lines as they become progressively heavier for example, should all be explained at the outset.

This section describes examples of good practice in relation to the detail design of both onshore and offshore structures. It is important to bear in mind that the most appropriate design **will reinforce the way in which a development reflects the landscape character of its location**. Detail design will therefore aim to reinforce the key characteristics of the landscape type, for example by reflecting colour and texture, by responding to landform shape and by using existing vegetation pattern.

The detail design information is divided into two sub sections:

- Water based structures
- Onshore developments

DETAIL DESIGN OF WATER-BASED STRUCTURES

The elements which make up water based developments include:

- main structures, such as cages, rafts, pontoons, jetties and nets
- mooring and navigation buoys
- longlines
- food storage and feeding structures
- lighting

Structures

- Dark muted colours are less obtrusive, and should be used for all structures wherever possible. It is a requirement of a Crown Estate lease that all installations other than for navigation purposes are dark matt grey in colour.
- Materials should be chosen which do not have a highly reflective surface, as this will catch the light and attract attention.
- Dark matt grey pontoons and jetties will blend into the landscape more subtly than brightly coloured or highly reflective materials.
- Handrails and other vertical structures should be kept as low as possible, within the requirements of health and safety regulations, to respect the horizontality of the water surface.
- Walk under nets, which can be up to two metres above the water surface, should generally be avoided.
- If there is more than one fish farm on a loch, they will appear less intrusive if the same types of cages and buoys are used. Storage facilities and shore bases should be shared where possible, reducing the amount of visual clutter.

Buoys and Longlines

- While navigation and corner buoys need to be brightly coloured and highly visible, other buoys should be of a consistent design and dark matt grey in colour.
- The pattern of buoys should, as far as possible, be kept simple and ordered within the loch space, and aligned reflecting the shape of the coastline.
- Where it is possible to align buoys to reflect the shape of the coastline, place buoys to emphasise the sense of 'line'.
- As the weight of the shellfish increases, the original, often quite small buoys need to be replaced with larger buoys, or the number of small buoys increased. Larger buoys can look out of scale in an intimate landscape and proposals should be assessed with this in mind.

Food Storage Systems

- The least intrusive system of food storage is hand feeding combined with a mobile storage raft mainly moored at the shore base.
- Structures such as sheds on cages will increase visibility and should be avoided.
- If storage structures are used on the cages, they should be stained or painted dark matt grey. Feed hoppers should be dark coloured and positioned as close to the water surface as possible
- Permanently moored large feeding stations and silos can be very visible and should be avoided, especially where the surroundings are low lying or the site is very exposed to view.
- Permanently moored large feeding stations and silos are slightly less intrusive if they are moored close to the corner of the cages, if they are as 'boat like' in scale and shape as possible and if they are coloured dark matt grey.

Lighting

- Security lighting can be very intrusive, creating unwanted light pollution. Where security measures are needed, to prevent vandalism or theft, operators should consider the use of infrared cameras, which eliminate the need for overhead lighting.
- Where overhead lighting is required, baffles or guards should be fitted to reduce the extent of light emission.
- Underwater lighting, used for photoperiod manipulation, is less intrusive, although it can create an eerie glow. However, in some areas, such as those valued for their sense of wildness, even subsea lighting may be unacceptable.

DETAIL DESIGN OF ONSHORE FACILITIES

Onshore facilities are not always required for aquaculture developments, and at the outset, developers should consider whether a base is necessary, or whether it is possible to share existing infrastructure.

Onshore bases may have a significant impact on the landscape, not least because they have the potential to be permanent structures. The implications of siting and design therefore have to be considered in terms of their long term impact.

In addition to buildings, a base may need lifting gear, a new access road and a power supply, all of which can accumulate to make a very significant impact, especially in an area with few or even no built structures. In some circumstances, consultees may be more concerned about the potential impact of an onshore facility than offshore cages or rafts.

Onshore facilities include:
- buildings
- net cleaning facilities
- slipways
- access tracks, external storage and vehicle parking

Buildings

- Redundant buildings can offer the opportunity for conversion into offices and storage sheds. The reuse of redundant buildings or slipways can often make a positive contribution to the landscape.
- New buildings should be sited to take advantage of natural landform and vegetation which will create a setting.
- Consider an innovative and ecologically sound building style if new build is required, in discussion with the local planning authority.
- Ensure that storage space is big enough to accommodate all storage needs, either through well scaled buildings or organised and adequate external storage space. Car parking areas, too, often need to be larger than at first considered.
- The size of shore based buildings and compounds should reflect the form and scale of other buildings. Buildings which are large will stand out, and should be orientated and aligned to fit in with existing settlement pattern.
- If a large storage shed is required, consider breaking up the mass of the building to reduce its scale.
- Avoid excavating a steep slope and excessive underbuilding, and fit the buildings into the gradient.

Other Infrastructure

- Even if existing buildings are not available for re use, consider using existing access tracks and other infrastructure such as slipways if possible.
- Tall lifting gear, and infrastructure which is particularly industrial in character is difficult to accommodate in more rural coastal landscapes.
- Likewise, large industrial-scale net cleaning stations need to be sited where the visual intrusion and smells do not adversely affect landscape character or experience of a place.
- Aim to create an appropriate setting for buildings by using fence materials and designs which relate to the character of the landscape. Avoid urban and suburban solutions.
- Although they may take longer to establish than 'instant' fencing barriers, well established and maintained planting may be more effective in the long term. At some sites, fencing could be used to create a setting for a building until planting is established.

This guidance describes and promotes the landscape character and design issues which it is appropriate to consider when developing a new fish or shellfish farm, or when extending an existing one.

Further advice on landscape issues raised by this guidance is available from SNH local and regional offices, and from Local Planning Authorities. Local contact addresses and telephone numbers are available from the relevant telephone directory. Other useful addresses are set out in Appendix 2 of this document.

The issues raised in this guidance serve to emphasise that good detail design alone cannot limit the impact of a structure – it is very important that developments are in locations where structures and activity are appropriate in the first place. Only this, combined with well sited, appropriately scaled and carefully laid out facilities will ensure that aquaculture development is successfuly integrated into the Scottish landscape.

Bibliography

Cobham Resource Consultants with Fisheries Development Ltd. 1987. An Environmental Assessment of Fish Farms. Countryside Commission for Scotland.

Cobham Resource Consultants. 1992. Landscape Issues in Relation to Marine and Freshwater Fish Farms. Final report to the Scottish Office Environment Department and the Countryside Commission for Scotland.

Environmental Resource Management. 1996. Landscape assessment of Argyll and the Firth of Clyde. Scottish Natural Heritage Review No 78.

Environmental Resources Management. 1998. Lochaber: landscape assessment. Scottish Natural Heritage Review No 77.

Stanton, C. 1996. Caithness and Sutherland landscape assessment. Scottish Natural Heritage Review No 103.

Stanton, C. 1996. Skye and Lochalsh landscape assessment. Scottish Natural Heritage Review No 71.

The Crown Estate. 1998. Environmental Assessment Guidance Manual for Marine Fish Farmers

The Scottish Office Agriculture Environment and Fisheries Department in association with the Crown Estate Commission and the Convention of Scottish Local Authorities 1998. Interim Scheme for the Licensing of Fish Farms in Scottish Waters. Policy Guidance Note.

The Scottish Office Agriculture Environment and Fisheries Department in association with the Crown Estate Commission and the Convention of Scottish Local Authorities 1998. Interim Scheme for the Licensing of Fish Farms in Scottish Waters. Advice Note: Marine Fish Farming and the Environment

The Scottish Office Agriculture Environment and Fisheries Department in association with the Crown Estate Commission and the Convention of Scottish Local Authorities. 1998. Interim Scheme for the Licensing of Fish Farms in Scottish Waters. Policy Guidance Note

The Scottish Office Development Department. 1997. National Planning Policy Guideline NPPG 13: Coastal Planning

The Scottish Office Development Department. 1999. National Planning Policy Guideline NPPG 14: Natural Heritage

The Scottish Office Development Department. 1999. National Planning Policy Guideline NPPG 15: Rural Development

The Scottish Office Development Department. 1993. Planning Advice Note 39: Farm and Forestry Buildings

The Scottish Office Development Department. 1997. Planning Advice Note 51: Planning and Environmental Protection

The Scottish Office Development Department. 1999. Planning Advice Note 53: Classifying the Coast for Planning Purposes

List of abbreviations

CCS	Countryside Commission for Scotland, now incorporated into SNH
CE	Crown Estate
EIA	Environmental Impact Assessment
HIDB	Highlands and Islands Development Board, now Highlands and Islands Enterprise
NSA	National Scenic Area, an area designated because of its spectacular scenic qualities
SEPA	Scottish Environmental Protection Agency
SNH	Scottish Natural Heritage
SOED	Scottish Office Education Department
SOAEFD	The Scottish Office Agriculture, Environmental and Fisheries Department
SERAD	The Scottish Executive Rural Affairs Department
SEDD	The Scottish Executive Development Department, which has national responsibilities for planning.
SQS	Scottish Quality Salmon (Formerly Scottish Salmon Growers Association)

Appendix 1: COMPLEMENTARY DOCUMENTS

An Environmental Assessment of Fish Farms (1986)	Commissioned by: CCS CEC HIDB SSGA	A comprehensive report on the extent, location, nature and visual impact of fish farms in the mid 1980s
Landscape Issues in Relation to Marine and Freshwater Fish Farms (1992)	Commissioned by: SOED CCS	An advice note to encourage sensitive siting, design and management of fish farms
Environmental Assessment Guidance Manual for Marine Salmon Farmers (1998)	CEC (now CE)	A Guidance Manual to explain EIA in relation to fish farming. It explains the system, and contains checklists of issues to be covered in EIA
National Planning Policy Guideline 13 'Coastal Planning' (1997)	Scottish Office Development Department	Outlines the Government's planning policy on development along the coast
Planning Advice Note PAN 53 'Classifying the Coast for Planning Purposes' (1999)	Scottish Office Development Department	Explains to Local Authorities how to develop coastal zones for planning purposes.
Interim Scheme for the Licensing of Marine Fish Farms in Scottish Waters (1998)	Scottish Office Agriculture, Environment and Fisheries Dept (now SERAD)	Explains the procedures for obtaining authorisation for setting up marine fish farms
Locational Guidelines for the Authorisation of Marine Fish Farms in Scottish Waters: 'Marine Fish Farming and the Environment'	Scottish Executive Rural Affairs Department, Fisheries Group	Explains government policy on marine fish farming, including guidance on locating fish farms and EIA. Gives Advice Note descriptive background, and maps of Category 1, Category 2 and Other Areas. Explains and provides practical advice on all environmental effects and constraints.
Scotland's Scenic Heritage (1978)	CCS (now SNH)	Lists National Scenic Areas, describes their character and contains maps showing their extent.
Guidelines for Landscape and Visual Impact Assessment (1995)	Institute of Environmental Assessment and the Landscape Institute	Offers guidance and advice on landscape and visual impact assessment, with examples
National Planning Policy Guideline 14 'Natural Heritage' (1999)	Scottish Office Development Department	Outlining the Governments planning policy on the natural heritage

Appendix 2: USEFUL ADDRESSES

The Crown Estate
10 Charlotte Square
Edinburgh
EH2 4DR

Scottish Executive Development Department
Planning Division
Victoria Quay
Edinburgh
EH6 6QQ

Scottish Executive Rural Affairs Department
Fisheries Group
Pentland House
47 Robbs Loan
Edinburgh
EH14 1TY

Scottish Natural Heritage (North)
27 Ardconnel Terrace
Inverness
IV2 3AE

Scottish Natural Heritage (West)
Caspian House
2 Mariner Court
8 South Avenue
Clydebank Business Park
Clydebank
G81 2NR

Scottish Natural Heritage
Research and Advisory Services
2/5 Anderson Place
Edinburgh
EH6 5NP

Scottish Quality Salmon
Durn
Isla Road
Perth
PH2 7HG

The Landscape Institute
6-8 Bernard Mews
London
SW11 1QU